Ballads

Wise Publications
London/New York/Paris/Sydney

Exclusive Distributors:
Music Sales Limited
8/9 Frith Street, London W1V 5TZ, England.
Music Sales Pty Limited
120 Rothschild Avenue, Rosebery, NSW 2018, Australia.

This book © Copyright 1992 by
Wise Publications
Order No.AM89944
ISBN 0-7119-3090-2

Music engraved by Interactive Sciences Limited, Gloucester.
Cover designed by Hutton Staniford
Music arranged by Stephen Duro
Compiled by Peter Evans

Music Sales' complete catalogue lists thousands of titles and is free from your local music shop,
or direct from Music Sales Limited. Please send a cheque/postal order for £1.50 for postage to:
Music Sales Limited, Newmarket Road, Bury St. Edmunds, Suffolk IP33 3YB.

Your Guarantee of Quality:

As publishers, we strive to produce every book to the highest commercial standards.

All the music has been freshly engraved and the book has been carefully designed to minimise
awkward page turns and to make playing from it a real pleasure.

Particular care has been given to specifying acid-free, neutral-sized paper which has not been
elemental chlorine bleached but produced with special regard for the environment.
Throughout, the printing and binding have been planned to ensure a sturdy,
attractive publication which should give years of enjoyment.

If your copy fails to meet our high standards, please inform us and we will gladly replace it.

Printed in the United Kingdom by
Halstan & Co Limited, Amersham, Buckinghamshire.

Annie's Song

Words & Music by John Denver

die in your arms. _____ Let me lay down be -
walk in the rain. _____ Like a storm in the

side you, _____ let me al - ways be with you, _____
des - ert, _____ Like a sleep - y blue o - cean _____

_____ Come let me love you, _____
_____ You fill up my sen - ses, _____

_____ come love me a - gain. _____ You
_____ come fill me a -

fill up my gain.

Candle In The Wind

Words & Music by Elton John & Bernie Taupin

made you   change   your name_____
Mar - i - lyn was found in the nude_____

And it   seems to me   you

lived your life_____ like a   can - dle in___ the wind_____   Nev - er   know - ing who to

cling to   when the   rain set in_____   And I   would have liked___ to have known___

_____ you but___ I was just___   a kid___   Your   can - dle had burned_____ out

long be-fore___ your   leg-end ev - er did.___

To Coda

8

D.% al Coda

Coda

9

Didn't We Almost Have It All

Words & Music by Michael Masser & Will Jennings

D.% al Coda

Coda

Feelings (Dime)

Words & Music by Morris Albert & Louis Gaste

Moderately

14

Goodbye To Love

Words by John Bettis, Music by Richard Carpenter

Moderately

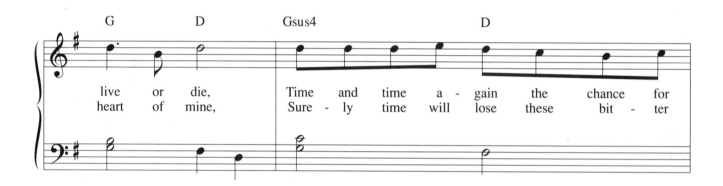

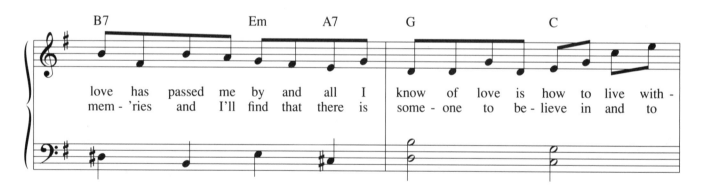

I'll say good - bye to love.

Ah

Ah

I'm Not In Love

Words & Music by Eric Stewart & Graham Gouldman

Hey Jude

Words & Music by John Lennon & Paul McCartney

23

How Deep Is Your Love

Words & Music by Barry Gibb, Robin Gibb & Maurice Gibb

Imagine

Words & Music by John Lennon

Killing Me Softly With His Song

Words by Norman Gimbel, Music by Charles Fox

Slowly

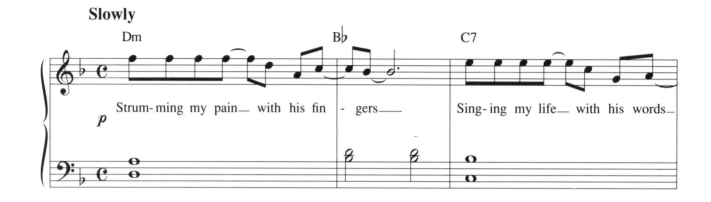

Nights In White Satin

Words & Music by Justin Hayward

Nights in white sat - in_____ nev - er reach - ing the end,
Gaz - ing at peo - ple,_____ some hand in hand,

Let - ters I've writ - ten_____ nev - er mean - ing to send.
Just what I'm going through_____ they can't un - der - stand.

Beau - ty I'd al - ways missed with these eyes_____ be - fore,
Some try to tell me_____ thoughts they can - not de - fend,

Just what the truth is_____ I can't say an - y - more_____ 'cause I
Just what you want to be, you'll be in the end,_____ and I

32

Let's Put It All Together

Words & Music by Hugo Perreti, Luigi Creatore & George David Weiss

is.　　Love like this nev - er hap - pened be - fore,＿ per - fect＿ and

true.　　Day by day we've been feel - in' it more,＿ you love me＿ and

I love you.　Let's put it all to - geth - er.＿

Let's put it all to - geth - er.＿ Let's put it all to -

geth - er,＿ girl, 'cause lov - in' is all there＿ is.

Something's Gotten Hold Of My Heart

Words & Music by Roger Cook & Roger Greenaway

Moderately

The First Time Ever I Saw Your Face

Words & Music by Ewan MacColl

41

The Long And Winding Road

Words & Music by John Lennon & Paul McCartney

Your Song

Words & Music by Elton John and Bernie Taupin

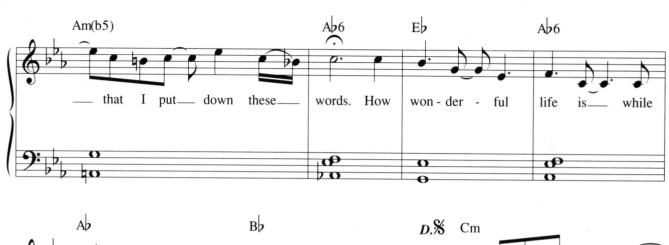

that I put down these words. How won-der-ful life is while

you-'re in the world.
7.8. I hope you don't mind

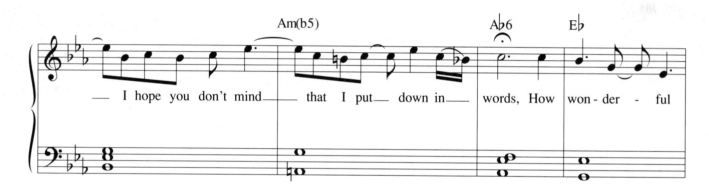

I hope you don't mind that I put down in words, How won-der-ful

life is while you-'re in the world.

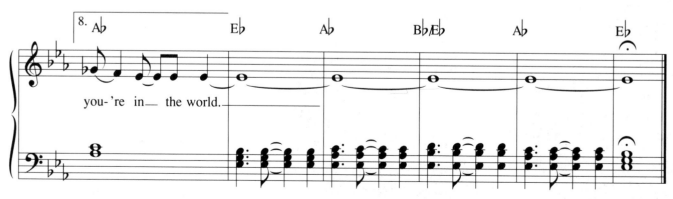

you-'re in the world.

9/98 (31926)

Each volume is specially arranged by Stephen Duro in extra-easy keys, so that the music fits comfortably to your hands, and includes lyrics (where appropriate) and chord symbols.

Collect the full series...

Abba *Order No. AM91038*
Bach *Order No. AM91041*
Ballads *Order No. AM89944*
Beethoven *Order No. AM91042*
Blues *Order No. AM91507*
Children's Songs *Order No. AM89953*
Richard Clayderman *Order No. AM91501*
Classics *Order No. AM89927*

Simply, the easiest books of popular music for piano **ever!**

Christmas *Order No. AM91509*
Folk Songs *Order No. AM91366*
Handel *Order No. AM91299*
Love Themes *Order No. AM91508*
Marches *Order No. AM91365*
Mozart *Order No. AM91043*
Operatic Arias *Order No. AM91312*
Pops *Order No. AM89939*
Rock 'n' Roll *Order No. AM91040*
Show Tunes *Order No. AM91039*
Symphonic Themes *Order No. AM91313*
Hits of the 50s *Order No. AM91502*
Hits of the 60s *Order No. AM91503*
Hits of the 70s *Order No. AM91504*
Hits of the 80s *Order No. AM91505*
The Beatles *Order No. AM89912*
The Beatles 2 *Order No. NO90571*
The Carpenters *Order No. AM91500*
TV Themes *Order No. AM89968*
Viennese Waltzes *Order No. AM91314*

Available from all good music shops

In case of difficulty, please contact:
Music Sales Limited
Newmarket Road,
Bury St. Edmunds,
Suffolk IP33 3YB, England
Telephone: 0284 702600
Fax: 0284 768301

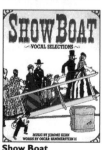